I Want to Play This!

Story by Catherine Baker
Illustrated by Sharon Harmer

Daisy

Zac

Once there was a boy called Alfie and he was feeling a little bit shy and the girl he met was called Sally. The cat was called Rubix

Sally toor Rubix outside but Alfie didn't want to play with the cat

Alfie wanted to play with his cars but Sally didn't want to play.

Then Alfie spotted a bush and said "we should play in it"

And then they made
a den and Alfie got
to play with his cars
and Sally played with

Rubix

They played until the end of the day.